THE
Indispensable
CALVIN
AND
HOBBES

A Calvin and Hobbes Treasury by
BILL WATTERSON
Includes cartoons from *The Revenge of the Baby-Sat*
and *Scientific Progress Goes "Boink"*

SCHOLASTIC INC.
New York Toronto London Auckland Sydney

Calvin and Hobbes is distributed internationally
by Universal Press Syndicate.

ISBN 0-590-47179-1

12 11 10 9 8 7 6 5 4 3 2   3 4 5 6 7 8/9

Printed in the U.S.A.   02

First Scholastic printing, February 1993

I made a big decision a little while ago.
I don't remember what it was, which prob'ly goes to show
That many times a simple choice can prove to be essential
Even though it often might appear inconsequential.

I must have been distracted when I left my home because
Left or right I'm sure I went. (I wonder which it was!)
Anyway, I never veered: I walked in that direction
Utterly absorbed, it seems, in quiet introspection.

For no reason I can think of, I've wandered far astray.
And that is how I got to where I find myself today.

Explorers are we, intrepid and bold,
Out in the wild, amongst wonders untold.
Equipped with our wits, a map, and a snack,
We're searching for fun and we're on the right track!

My mother has eyes on the back of her head!
I don't quite believe it, but that's what she said.
She explained that she'd been so uniquely endowed
To catch me when I did Things Not Allowed.
I think she must also have eyes on her rear.
I've noticed her hindsight is unusually clear.

At night my mind does not much care
If what it thinks is here or there.
It tells me stories it invents
And makes up things that don't make sense.
I don't know why it does this stuff.
The real world seems quite weird enough.

What if my bones were in a museum,
Where aliens paid good money to see 'em?
And suppose that they'd put me together all wrong,
Sticking bones on to bones where they didn't belong!

Imagine phalanges, pelvis, and spine
Welded to mandibles that once had been mine!
With each misassemblage, the error compounded,
The aliens would draw back in terror, astounded!

Their textbooks would show me in grim illustration,
The most hideous thing ever seen in creation!
The museum would commission a model in plaster
Of ME, to be called, "Evolution's Disaster"!

And paleontologists there would debate
Dozens of theories to help postulate
How man survived for those thousands of years
With teeth-covered arms growing out of his ears!

Oh, I hope that I'm never in such manner displayed,
No matter HOW much to see me the aliens paid.

I did not want to go with them.
Alas, I had no choice.
This was made quite clear to me
In threat'ning tones of voice.

I protested mightily
And scrambled 'cross the floor.
But though I grabbed the furniture,
They dragged me out the door.

In the car, I screamed and moaned.
I cried my red eyes dry.
The window down, I yelled for help
To people we passed by.

Mom and Dad can make the rules
And certain things forbid,
But I can make them wish that they
Had never had a kid.

Now I'm in bed,
The sheets pulled to my head.
My tiger is here making Zs.
He's furry and hot.
He takes up a lot
Of the bed and he's hogging the breeze.

17

27

45

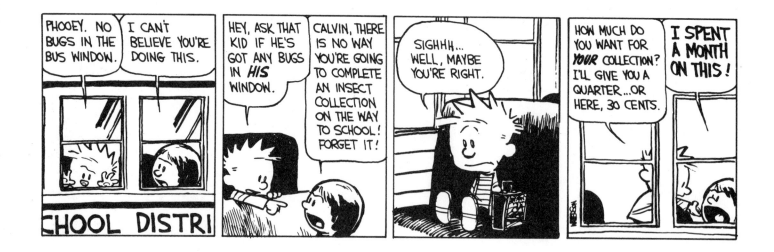

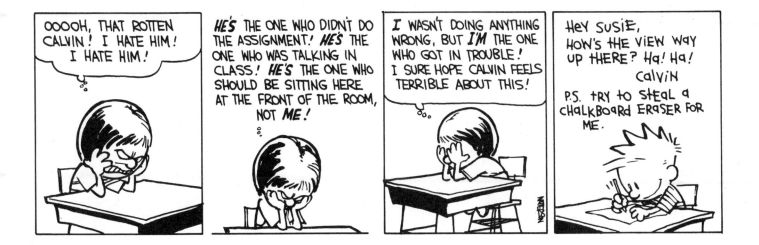

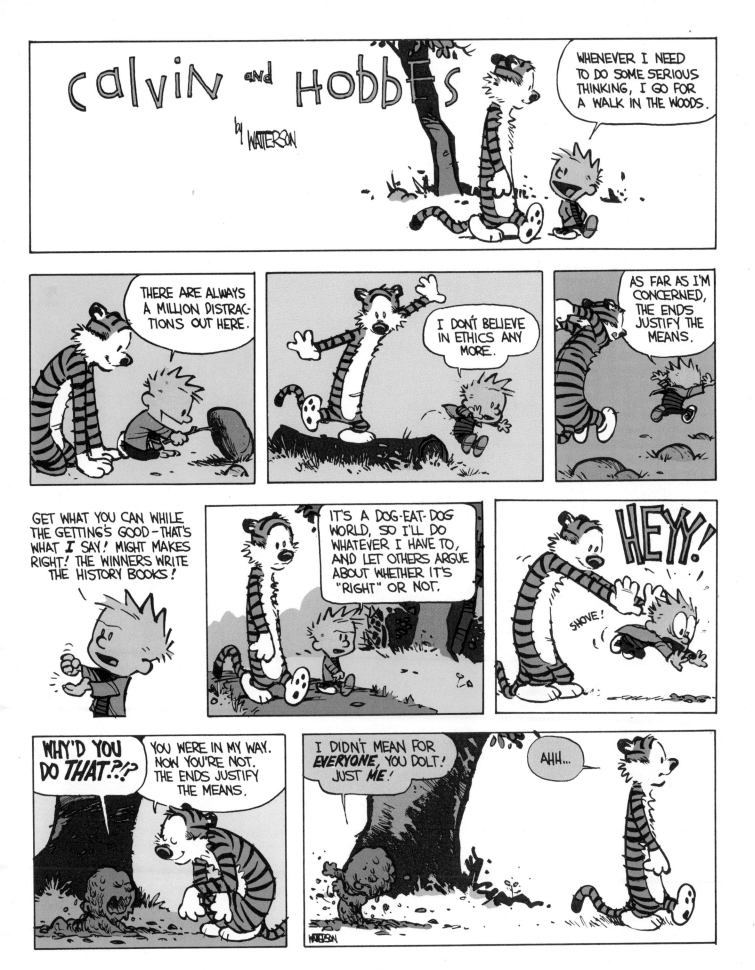

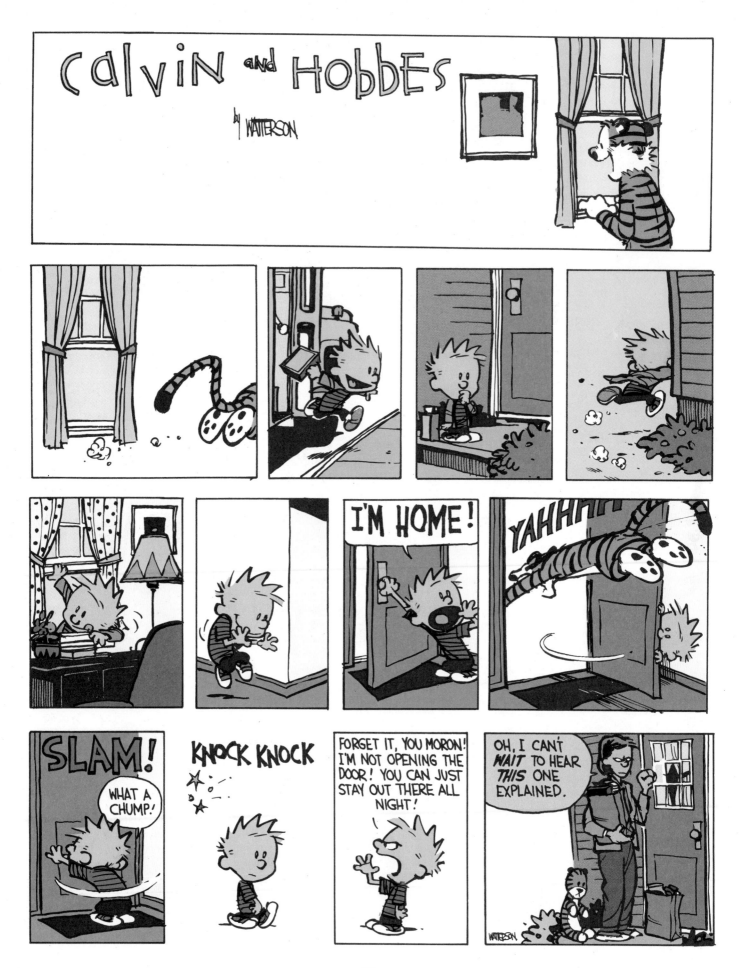

72

IS CALVIN ASLEEP?

YES, HE'S SNUGGLED UP WITH HOBBES.

BOY, I DON'T KNOW HOW *I'M* EVER GOING TO SLEEP.

ME NEITHER. I CAN'T GET OVER WHAT'S HAPPENED.

THE IDEA OF SOME CRAZY STRANGER GOING THROUGH OUR HOUSE... *BRRRR!!* I WISH *I* HAD A BIG STUFFED ANIMAL TO FEEL SAFE WITH.

I GUESS YOU'LL HAVE TO DO.

SO WHAT DO *I* GET TO SNUGGLE? HOW COME *I'M* THE GROWN-UP??

THIS IS GOING TO BE A LONG NIGHT.

MY HEART JUMPS AT THE SLIGHTEST SOUND. IT'S ALMOST 2, AND I'M WIDE AWAKE.

WHEN SOMEONE BREAKS INTO YOUR HOME, IT SHATTERS YOUR LAST ILLUSION OF SECURITY. IF YOU'RE NOT SAFE IN YOUR OWN HOME, YOU'RE NOT SAFE ANYWHERE.

A MAN'S HOME IS HIS CASTLE, BUT IT SHOULDN'T HAVE TO BE A FORTRESS.

ARE YOU STILL AWAKE TOO?

MM-HMM. I WAS THINKING.

IT'S FUNNY... WHEN I WAS A KID, I THOUGHT GROWN-UPS NEVER WORRIED ABOUT ANYTHING. I TRUSTED MY PARENTS TO TAKE CARE OF EVERYTHING, AND IT NEVER OCCURRED TO ME THAT THEY MIGHT NOT KNOW HOW.

I FIGURED THAT ONCE YOU GREW UP, YOU AUTOMATICALLY KNEW WHAT TO DO IN ANY GIVEN SCENARIO.

I DON'T THINK I'D HAVE BEEN IN SUCH A HURRY TO REACH ADULTHOOD IF I'D KNOWN THE WHOLE THING WAS GOING TO BE AD-LIBBED.

 GOOD NEWS, HOBBES! I'M STARTING A SECRET CLUB, AND YOU CAN BE IN IT! OH, BOY!

 IT'LL BE GREAT! WE'LL THINK OF SECRET NAMES FOR OURSELVES, SECRET CODES FOR OUR SECRET CORRESPONDENCE, A SECRET HANDSHAKE,...

 WE'LL HAVE A SECRET CLUBHOUSE WITH A SECRET KNOCK TO GET IN, AND WE'LL DO BIG, SECRETIVE THINGS! WHY ALL THE SECRECY?

 PEOPLE PAY MORE ATTENTION TO YOU WHEN THEY THINK YOU'RE UP TO SOMETHING.

OK, THE FIRST THING WE NEED IS A NAME FOR OUR SECRET CLUB.

LET'S CALL IT "THE HOBBES FAN CLUB"! THE HOBBES FAN CLUB?! GIVE ME A BREAK! I'M SURE!!

THIS IS A TOP-SECRET SOCIETY! THE NAME SHOULD BE SOMETHING *MYSTERIOUS*! SOMETHING VAGUELY OMINOUS AND CHILLING!

SOMETHING LIKE, "THE SINISTER ICY BLACK HAND OF DEATH CLUB"? I STILL LIKE MY IDEA BETTER.

I'VE GOT IT! WE'LL CALL OUR CLUB G.R.O.S.S. — *GET RID OF SLIMY GIRLS!* THAT WAY, SUSIE DERKINS CAN'T JOIN!

IS SHE SLIMY? *ALL* GIRLS ARE SLIMY. NOW THE FIRST ORDER OF BUSINESS IS TO ELECT OFFICERS.

I GET TO BE PRESIDENT! I GET TO BE PRESIDENT! OH, NO YOU DON'T! THIS WHOLE CLUB WAS *MY* IDEA, SO *I* GET TO BE PRESIDENT.

OK, THEN I GET TO BE KING AND TYRANT. HEY, NO! *THAT'S* WHAT *I* WANT TO BE! YOU CAN BE PRESIDENT!

Panel 1: DO YOU THINK WE'RE SAFE? SHOULD WE CLIMB HIGHER? / IT'S HARD TO SAY WITH BEARS.

Panel 2: THERE IT IS! THE BEAR'S COMING OUT OF THE BRUSH! OH NO! IT LOOKS LIKE IT'S ON ITS HIND LEGS! BEARS STAND UP ONLY WHEN THEY'RE REALLY MAD!!

Panel 3: WAIT, THAT'S NOT A BEAR. THAT'S YOUR MOM! / AAUGHH! EVEN WORSE! CLIMB HIGHER! CLIMB HIGHER!

Panel 4: *THERE* YOU ARE. COME DOWN SO I CAN TALK TO YOU. / NO. YOU'LL KILL US. WE'RE RUNNING AWAY.

Panel 5: I'M NOT GOING TO KILL YOU. I JUST WANT TO FIND OUT WHAT HAPPENED. ARE YOU OK? WAS ANYONE HURT? / NO ONE WAS HURT. WE WERE PUSHING THE CAR INTO THE DRIVE AND IT KEPT ROLLING.

Panel 6: THE CAR DIDN'T HIT ANYTHING? / IT JUST WENT ACROSS THE ROAD AND INTO THE DITCH. THAT'S WHEN WE TOOK OFF.

Panel 7: WELL, THE TOW TRUCK PULLED IT OUT, AND THERE'S NO DAMAGE, SO YOU CAN COME HOME NOW. / FIRST LET'S HEAR YOU SAY YOU LOVE ME.

Panel 8: BOY, HOBBES, ISN'T IT FUNNY HOW THINGS SOMETIMES WORK OUT? MOM AND DAD SAW RIGHT AWAY THAT WHAT HAPPENED TO THE CAR WAS AN ACCIDENT.

Panel 9: THEY WERE SO RELIEVED NO ONE GOT HURT THAT ALL WE GOT WAS A LECTURE ON SAFETY AND ASKING PERMISSION. THEY DIDN'T EVEN RAISE THEIR VOICES.

Panel 10: PARENTS ARE SURE INSCRUTABLE, HUH? SEND THEIR CAR OVER A DITCH AND YOU DON'T EVEN GET YELLED AT.

Panel 11: ...BUT TRY KEEPING LIVE WORMS IN YOUR DAD'S... / LET'S NOT TALK ABOUT THAT, OK?!

WHAT KIND OF DINOSAUR DID YOU SAY THIS WAS?

IT'S A STEGO-SAURUS!

HE LOOKS PRETTY FEROCIOUS.

NO, HE WAS A PLANT EATER. THE TAIL SPIKES WERE FOR SELF-DEFENSE.

OH. DID TYRANNOSAURS FIGHT THESE?

OF COURSE NOT, MOM! TYRANNOSAURS CAME MILLIONS OF YEARS LATER!

LOOK, TRY NOT TO EMBARRASS ME WHEN WE GO INSIDE, OK?

WHY ARE WE GOING HERE IF HE ALREADY KNOWS EVERY-THING?

LOOK, HOBBES, HERE'S AN ANCESTOR OF *YOURS!* A SABER-TOOTHED TIGER!

HA HA, I'LL BET *HE* WAS POPULAR! IF ANYONE NEEDED TO OPEN A CAN OF JUICE, THEY'D JUST PUT HIM OVER IT AND HIT HIM ON THE HEAD! HA HA!

HEE HEE, I'LL BET THEY DIED OUT BECAUSE THEY COULDN'T UNDERSTAND EACH OTHER! THEY PWOBABBY DOKKED WIKE DIFF! HA HA HA!

... ALL IN ALL, THOUGH, THEY WERE UNDOUBTEDLY THE PINNACLE OF PREHISTORIC EVOLUTION ..

LOOK, MOM, THE MUSEUM HAS A GIFT SHOP!

CAN I BUY SOMETHING? THEY'VE GOT DINOSAUR BOOKS, DINOSAUR MODELS, DINOSAUR T-SHIRTS, DINOSAUR POSTERS..

I DON'T THINK YOU NEED ANY MORE DINOSAUR STUFF, CALVIN.

BUT MOM, IT'S ALL *EDUCATIONAL!* YOU WANT ME TO *LEARN,* DON'T YOU??

BOY, SHE FELL FOR *THAT* ONE.

I'LL SAY! I WONDER IF WE COULD GET ANY BATMAN JUNK THIS WAY.

UH OH, CALVIN THE REPTILE IS IN TROUBLE!

AS AN ECTOTHERM, HIS BODY RELIES ON THE ENVIRONMENT TO WARM OR COOL ITS TEMPERATURE.

NOW THAT IT'S COLDER OUTSIDE, CALVIN'S BODY TEMPERATURE FALLS AND HE BECOMES SLUGGISH! HE'LL GO INTO TORPOR IF HE CAN'T FIND A WARM PLACE TO LIE!

LEAVE THE THERMOSTAT ALONE, AND PUT ON A SWEATER IF YOU'RE COLD.

I...I DON'T HAVE THE EN..ENERGY!

I HEARD THAT BIG CATS DON'T PURR.

THAT'S TRUE. WE'RE TOO FIERCE AND FEROCIOUS. WE DON'T EVER PURR.

WELL WHAT DO YOU CALL THE NOISE YOU MAKE WHEN YOU GET YOUR TUMMY RUBBED?!

GROWLING FRIENDLY-LIKE.

CALVIN, YOUR MOM AND I LOOKED OVER YOUR REPORT CARD, AND WE THINK YOU COULD BE DOING BETTER.

BUT I DON'T LIKE SCHOOL.

WHY NOT? YOU LIKE TO READ AND YOU LIKE TO LEARN. I KNOW YOU DO.

I MEAN, YOU'VE READ EVERY DINOSAUR BOOK EVER WRITTEN, AND YOU'VE LEARNED A LOT, RIGHT? READING AND LEARNING ARE FUN.

YEAH..

SO WHY DON'T YOU LIKE SCHOOL?

WE DON'T READ ABOUT DINOSAURS.

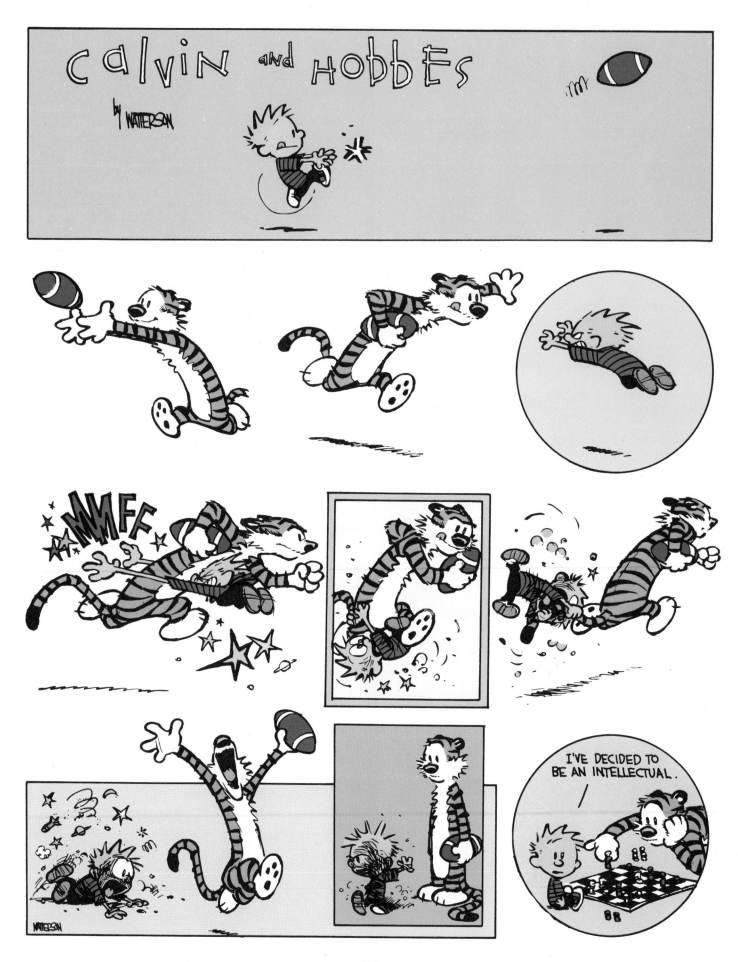

HOW TOUCHING.

135

140

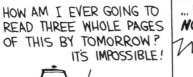

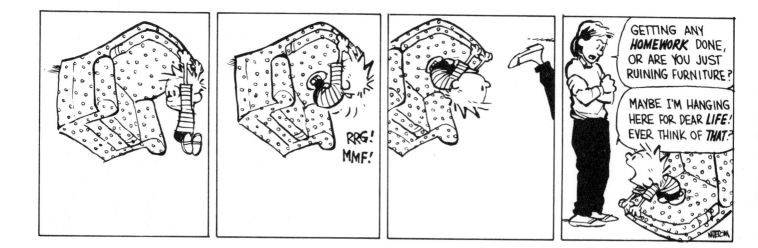

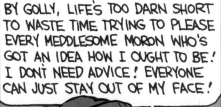

THIS IS THE PART OF WINTER I LIKE BEST... WHEN YOU COME INSIDE, FREEZING COLD AND SOAKED...

...AND YOU PUT ON FRESH DRY CLOTHES, AND RUN UP TO THE WARM KITCHEN, WHERE MOM'S GOT A STEAMING MUG OF HOT CHOCOLATE WAITING FOR YOU!

MOM? ... MOM?? HEY MOM!

"CALVIN, I'M NEXT DOOR. DON'T HAVE ANYTHING TO EAT, OR YOU'LL SPOIL YOUR APPETITE. MOM."

IT'S GOING TO BE A LONG, COLD, DARK WINTER.

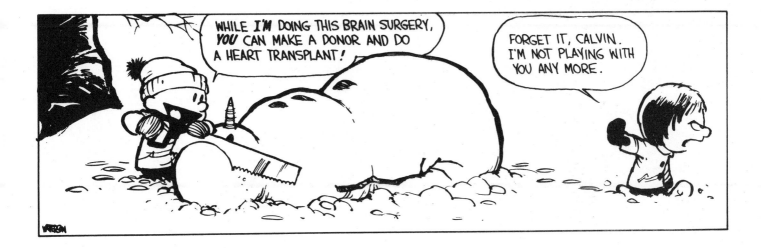

WHILE *I'M* DOING THIS BRAIN SURGERY, *YOU* CAN MAKE A DONOR AND DO A HEART TRANSPLANT!

FORGET IT, CALVIN. I'M NOT PLAYING WITH YOU ANY MORE.

Calvin and Hobbes

by WATTERSON

WHOSE BRILLIANT IDEA WAS IT TO TAKE A HIKE OUT IN THIS BITTER COLD?! HOW MUCH LONGER DO WE HAVE TO DO THIS?

I FEEL LIKE I'M IN "DR. ZHIVAGO."

ALL RIGHT, CALVIN. YOU'VE MADE YOUR POINT, I THINK.

I HATE THESE FORCED MARCHES! WHEN ARE WE GOING HOME?

THIS IS JUST A LITTLE WALK, CALVIN. THE EXERCISE IS GOOD FOR YOU.

BUT I'M *FREEZING!* IT MUST BE 80 BELOW! MY TOES ARE NUMB!

NUMB TOES BUILD CHARACTER.

YEAH? WELL, WHAT ABOUT FROSTBITE?! WHAT ABOUT HYPOTHERMIA?! WHAT ABOUT *DEATH*?! I SUPPOSE *THOSE* BUILD CHARACTER TOO! I CANT BELIEVE I'M OUT HERE!

THIS IS THE WORST DAY OF MY ENTIRE LIFE! I HATE THIS! ARENT WE GOING HOME YET? IT SEEMS LIKE WE'VE BEEN WALKING FOR HOURS!

CALVIN, WILL YOU *PLEASE* STOP GRIPING?

GRIPING? *I'M* NOT GRIPING! I'M JUST *OBSERVING* WHAT A MISERABLE EXPERIENCE THIS IS! BUT OK! *SURE!* AS LONG AS I'M TRUDGING HUNDREDS OF MILES FOR NO APPARENT REASON, I MIGHT AS WELL DO IT IN *SILENCE*, RIGHT?!

JUST BECAUSE I'M OUT IN THE ELEMENTS LIKE A COMPLETE IDIOT, WATCHING MY DIGITS TURN TO ICE AND FALL OFF, I SURE AS HECK WOULDN'T EVER WANT TO SPOIL THE...

WE'RE *HOME.*

WE'RE WHAT? OH LOOK, WE'RE HOME!

QUIZ:
Jack and Joe leave their homes at the same time and drive toward each other. Jack drives at 60 mph, while Joe drives at 30 mph. They pass each other in 10 minutes.

How far apart were Jack and Joe when they started?

IT WAS ANOTHER BAFFLING CASE. BUT THEN, YOU DON'T HIRE A **PRIVATE EYE** FOR THE **EASY** ONES...

I'D PLANNED TO TAKE THE DAY **OFF** AND SPEND TIME WITH A COUPLE OF **BUDDIES**. MY BUDDIES TRAVEL LIGHT AND THEY'RE FUN TO HAVE AROUND. ONE TRAVELS IN A HOLSTER, AND THE OTHER IN A HIP FLASK.

MY NAME IS **BULLET**. TRACER BULLET. WHAT PEOPLE **CALL** ME IS SOMETHING ELSE AGAIN. I'M A PRIVATE EYE. IT SAYS SO ON MY DOOR.

THE **LAST** THING I WANTED THIS MORNING WAS A **CASE** TO SOLVE, BUT THE DAME WHO BROUGHT IT WAS **PERSUASIVE**. MOST DAMES **ARE**, SOMEHOW.

GET TO WORK, CALVIN.

I TOLD HER IT WOULD COST HER FIFTY GREENBACKS A DAY, PLUS EXPENSES.

I STEPPED OUT INTO THE RAINY STREETS AND REVIEWED THE FACTS. THERE WEREN'T MANY.

TWO SAPS, JACK AND JOE, DRIVE TOWARD EACH OTHER AT 60 AND 30 MPH. AFTER 10 MINUTES, THEY PASS. I'M SUPPOSED TO FIND OUT HOW FAR APART THEY STARTED.

QUESTIONS POUR DOWN LIKE THE RAIN. WHO **ARE** THESE MUGS? WHAT WERE THEY TRYING TO ACCOMPLISH? WHY WAS JACK IN SUCH A HURRY? AND WHAT DIFFERENCE DOES IT MAKE WHERE THEY STARTED FROM??

I HAD A HUNCH THAT, BEFORE THIS WAS OVER, I'D BE SORRY I ASKED.

197

199

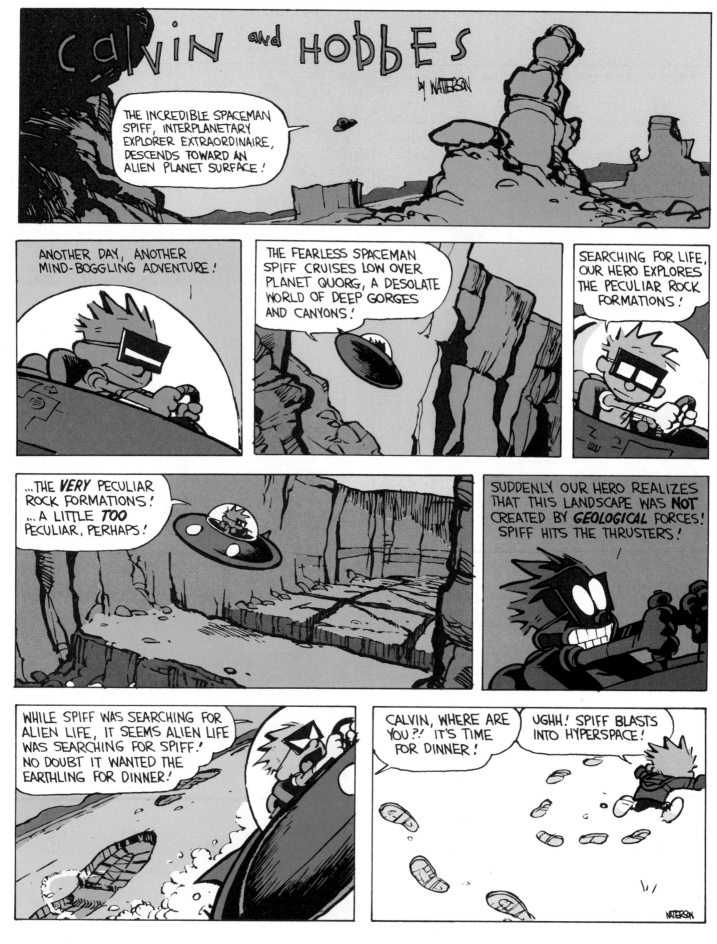

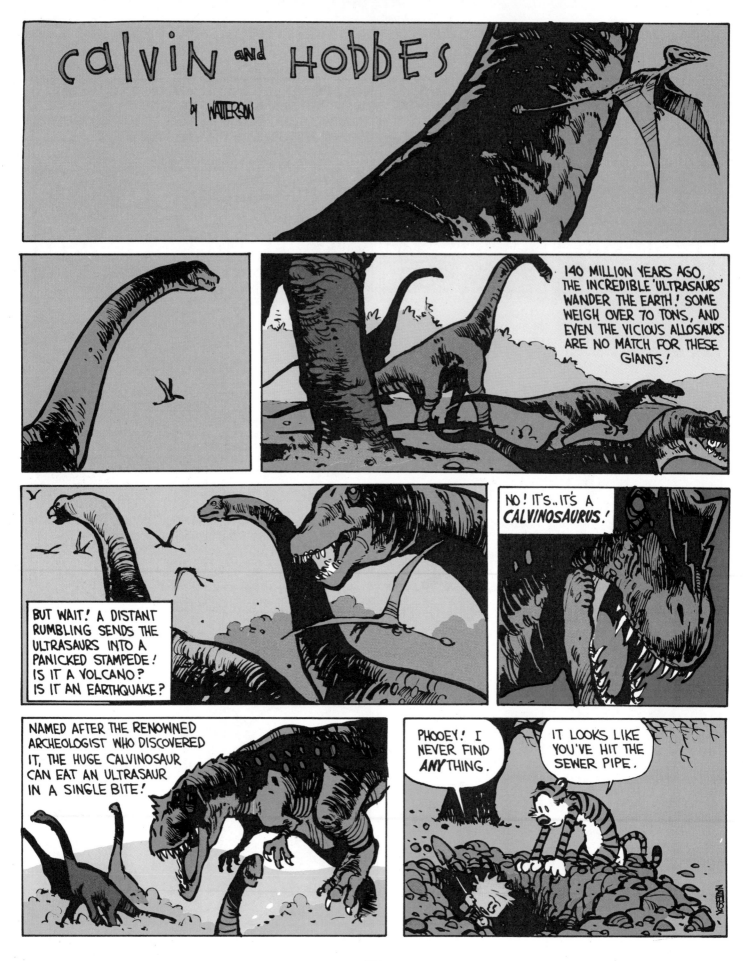

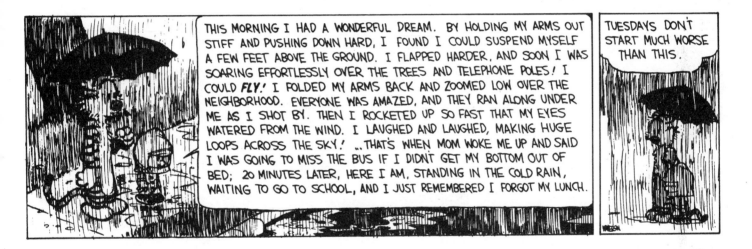

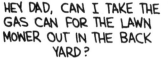

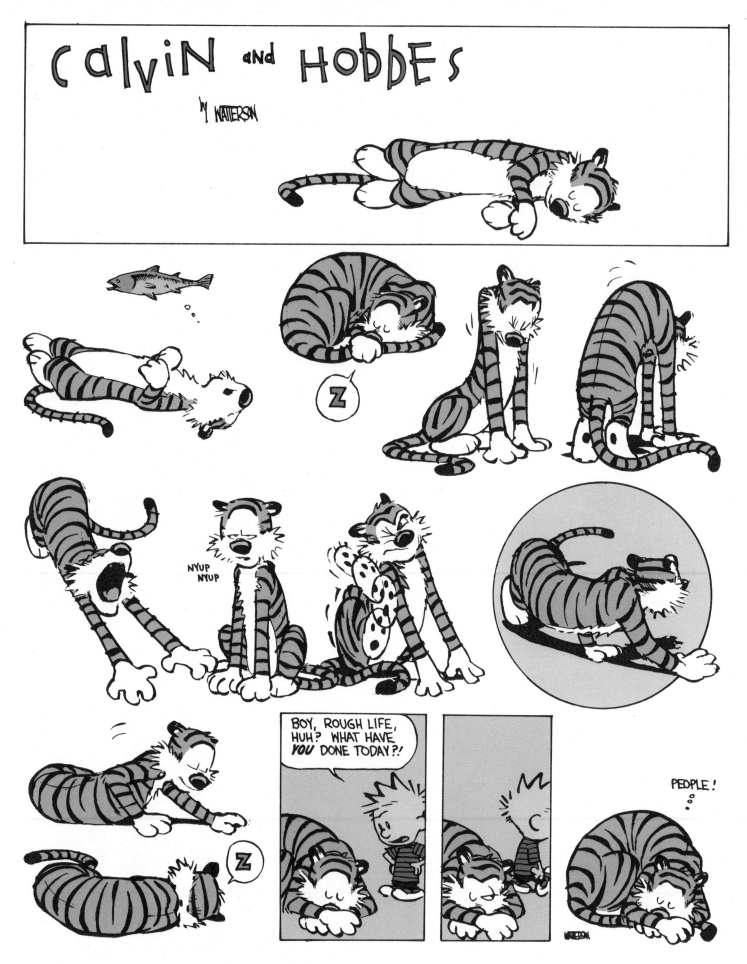

215

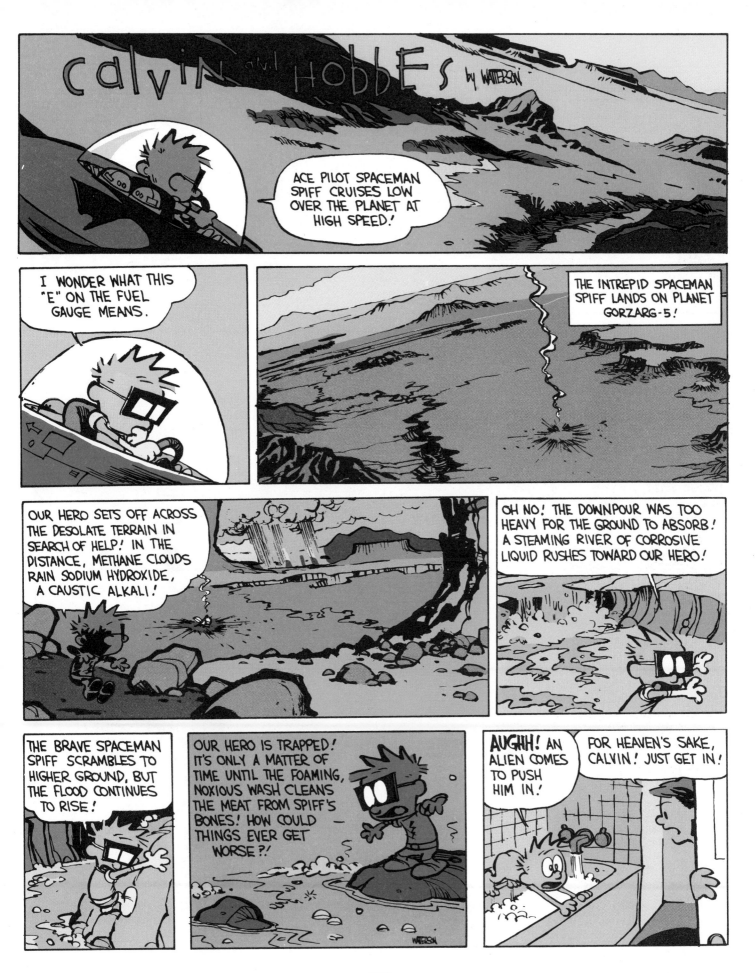

225

227

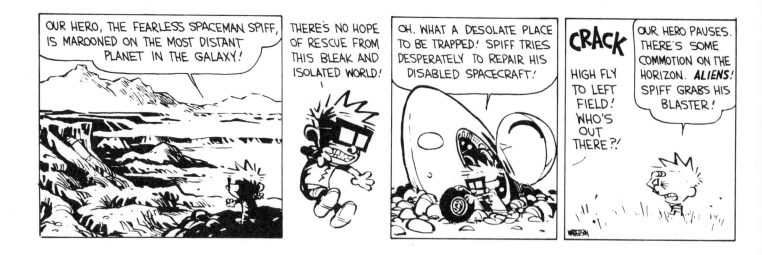

231

233

234

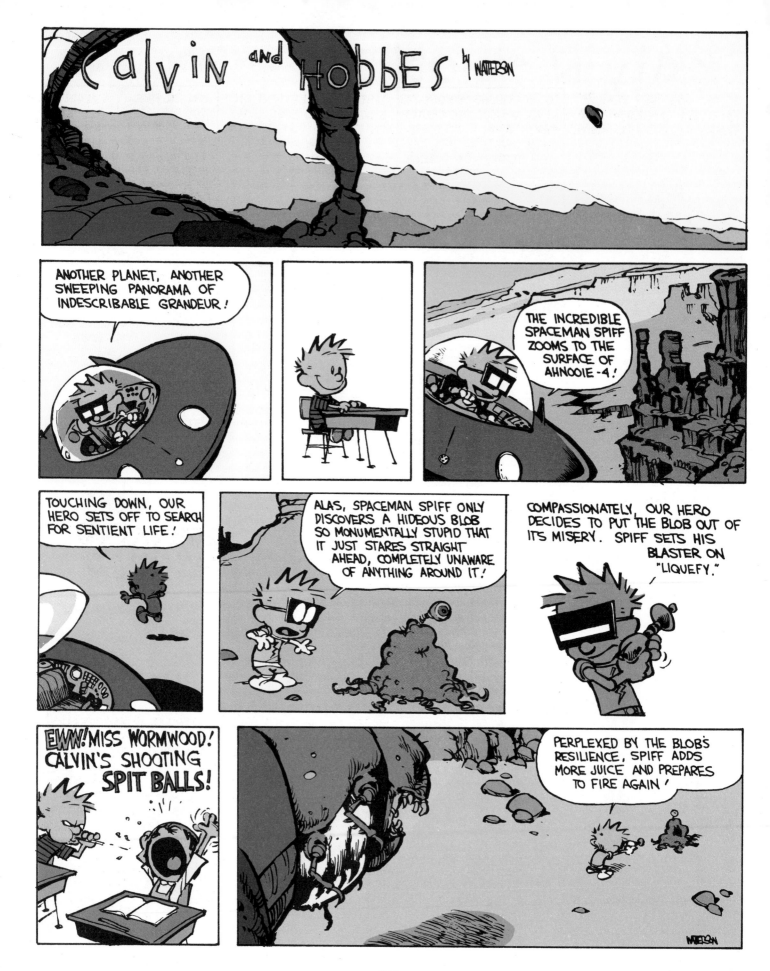

The End